THE NATURE OF
EXPERIENCE

UNIVERSITY OF DURHAM
PUBLICATIONS

THE NATURE OF EXPERIENCE

The Riddell Memorial Lectures
Thirtieth Series
delivered at King's College in the
University of Durham
on 12, 13, and 14 May 1958

BY

SIR RUSSELL BRAIN, Bt.

LONDON
OXFORD UNIVERSITY PRESS
NEW YORK TORONTO
1959

Oxford University Press, Amen House, London E.C.4

GLASGOW NEW YORK TORONTO MELBOURNE WELLINGTON
BOMBAY CALCUTTA MADRAS KARACHI KUALA LUMPUR
CAPE TOWN IBADAN NAIROBI ACCRA

PRINTED IN GREAT BRITAIN

PREFACE

I AM grateful to the Trustees for inviting me to deliver these lectures, which are a memorial to a philosopher. I am very much aware of my amateur status in philosophy, but if the expanding universe of knowledge is not to carry all the specialists into ever-increasing isolation from each other, and the rest of the world, some attempt must be made here and there to achieve a comprehensive view. I have therefore tried to do this in the field of perception.

I am indebted to the Literary Trustees of Walter de la Mare for permission to print a verse from one of his poems, and to John Lehmann, Ltd., for allowing me to reproduce a passage from Paul Valéry's *Dance and the Soul*.

CONTENTS

In your own Bosom you bear your Heaven
And Earth; & all you behold, tho' it appears Without, it is Within
In your Imagination, of which this World of Mortality is but a Shadow.

WILLIAM BLAKE, *Jerusalem*, plate 71

I

VISION AND FANTASY

I DECIDED on the subject of these lectures a year ago at Oxford. It was early spring, and I was there to deliver a lecture. Having an hour to spare I went into a bookshop to look round. Usually in a bookshop it is the individual books which catch the eye, but this time I suddenly became oppressed with the vast mass of the literature arranged there—thousands of books, books by the million words, books by the mile, books claiming to embody all human knowledge and wisdom, but defeating their object because no man lives long enough to read more than a small fraction of them, nor can anyone be sure that the ultimate secret is not contained in some volume he will never read. There were books about the past, showing how often man has changed his mind; and books on philosophy, showing that for 2,500 years philosophers have been disagreeing about much the same things; and there were books of poetry, showing that as long as man has been writing he has been using words to transcend the limits of speech, and still looks in much the same way upon nature, love, and death. Staggering a little, mentally, under the impact of so much 'information' I went out again into the street, past the heads of the Roman emperors, hollow-eyed with time, outside the Sheldonian Theatre, and down New College Lane. Beneath the statue of the Virgin over the gate I entered the College and walked round the garden, where the trees were breaking into leaf and the spring flowers beginning to colour the borders; and by then it was time for me to go on and deliver my lecture on a form of cancer. And as I looked back over the past quarter of an hour I thought how many modes of apprehension had presented themselves in that short time—in the bookshop all that is transmissible in words, art in the sculptured heads and the Virgin's statue, religion in the foundation dedicated to the Virgin, nature in the garden, science in my lecture, and, there too, hidden beneath the statistics, all the joys and sorrows embodied in the lives of those men and women whose deaths I was to discuss in so abstract a way.

And so I decided to talk to you about modes of apprehension. And I put the idea away, not having much time to devote to it, until a few months ago I sailed from Cape Town to England, and that gave me leisure to think. But it also meant that the subject-matter of my original reflections became mixed with new experiences, with the memories of a visit to South Africa, and the sights and sounds of the voyage. And through my thoughts dolphins gambolled, and flying-fish flashed, whales spouted, and albatrosses wheeled, radar showed me the invisible, and all against the unchanging changefulness of the sea.

I have begun by giving you an autobiographical account of the origin of these lectures. Even as such it is, of course, extremely incomplete, but it serves to stress at the outset my belief that a philosophy is an abstraction from an autobiography. Any air of impersonality which it may assume is fallacious. Philosophies illustrate the fairy story of the Emperor's clothes in reverse. The philosophy claims to be naked—the naked truth—but the eye of a child sees it to be wearing the oddest collection of old clothes, some inherited from the past, and some painstakingly made by the philosopher, like a caddis-worm, from such materials as he happened to have at hand. Indeed, we may come to the conclusion that the important thing about truth is not that it should be naked, but what clothes suit it best, and whether it should not sometimes dress up for special occasions.

I shall not begin by saying what I mean by apprehension; that, I hope, will emerge as these lectures go on. I will, however, quote a reference to it which occurs in a very familiar passage from Shakespeare, because those few lines are a supreme description of many of the things which we shall be considering.

HIPPOLYTA. 'Tis strange, my Theseus, that these lovers
    speak of.
THESEUS. More strange than true: I never may believe
    These antique fables, nor these fairy toys.
    Lovers and madmen have such seething brains,
    Such shaping fantasies, that apprehend
    More than cool reason ever comprehends.
    The lunatic, the lover and the poet
    Are of imagination all compact:
    One sees more devils than vast hell can hold,
    That is, the madman: the lover, all as frantic
    Sees Helen's beauty in a brow of Egypt:
    The poet's eye in a fine frenzy rolling,
    Doth glance from heaven to earth, from earth to heaven;
    And as imagination bodies forth
    The form of things unknown, the poet's pen
    Turns them to shapes, and gives to airy nothing
    A local habitation and a name.
    Such tricks hath strong imagination,
    That, if it would but apprehend some joy,
    It comprehends some bringer of that joy;
    Or in the night, imagining some fear,
    How easy is a bush supposed a bear!

HIPPOLYTA. But all the story of the night told over,
　　And all their minds transfigured so together,
　　More witnesseth than fancy's images,
　　And grows to something of great constancy;
　　But, howsoever, strange and admirable.

Here is all the raw material of these lectures, 'shaping fantasies' and 'apprehension', 'reason' and 'comprehension', perceptions, illusions, and hallucinations. The perceptual disorder of the lover, the status of the world of imagination, and the epistemological significance of the poet's pen will all claim our attention. Let us begin with perception.

It might have been thought that by now all the major questions relating to so familiar a process as perception would have been settled, yet how far this is from being true is illustrated by the regular appearance of discussions of it in books of philosophy and articles in *Mind* since the end of the war. We shall shortly have to consider how far the problems to which perception gives rise are, as some philosophers think, purely verbal, or empirical, or both. But whatever their origin the answers which people give to them lead to the most varied conclusions about the nature of the world. Let me give you three illustrations of this. Here is the famous passage in which Whitehead[1] describes the outcome of the views of Descartes and Locke.

The mind in apprehending also experiences sensations which, properly speaking, are projected by the mind alone. These sensations are projected by the mind so as to clothe appropriate bodies in external nature. Thus the bodies are perceived as with qualities which in reality do not belong to them, qualities which in fact are purely the offspring of the mind. Thus nature gets credit which should in truth be reserved for ourselves: the rose for its scent: the nightingale for its song: and the sun for its radiance. The poets are entirely mistaken. They should address their lyrics to themselves, and should turn them into odes of self-congratulation on the excellency of the human mind. Nature is a dull affair, soundless, scentless, colourless, merely the hurrying of material, endless, meaningless.

Then there are Eddington's[2] famous two tables.

One of them [he said] has been familiar to me from earliest years. It is a commonplace object of that environment which I call the world. How shall I describe it? It has extension; it is comparatively permanent; it is coloured; above all it is *substantial*. . . . Table number 2 is my scientific table. . . . It does not belong to the world previously mentioned—that world which spontaneously appears around me when I open my eyes, though how much of it is objective and how much subjective I do not here consider. . . . My scientific table is mostly emptiness. Sparsely scattered in that emptiness are numerous electric charges rushing about with great speed; but their combined bulk amounts to less than a billionth of the bulk of the table itself. . . . There is nothing *substantial* about my second table.

Bertrand Russell,[3] making broadly the same distinction as Eddington, draws the logical conclusion that Eddington's two tables must exist in two different spaces.

Naïve realism [he writes] identifies my percepts with physical things; it assumes that the sun of the astronomers is what I see. This involves identifying the spatial relations of my percepts with those of physical things. Many people retain this aspect of naïve realism though they have rejected all the rest. But this identification is indefensible. The spatial relations of physics hold between electrons, protons, neutrons, etc., which we do not perceive; the spatial relations of visual percepts hold between things that we do perceive, and in the last analysis between coloured patches. There is a rough correlation between physical space and visual space, but it is very rough.

And again

the distinction between 'seeing the sun' as a mental event, and the immediate object of my seeing, is now generally rejected as invalid, and in this view I concur. But many of those who take the view that I take on this point nevertheless inconsistently adhere to some form of naïve realism. If my seeing of the sun is identical with the sun that I see, then the sun that I see is not the astronomers' sun. For exactly the same reason, the tables and chairs that I see, if they are identical with my seeing of them, are not located where physics says they are, but where my seeing is.

A similar distinction, Russell points out, must be drawn between our own bodies as perceived objects and as physical objects, and this is a point to which I shall return. Finally, he concludes:

One of the difficulties which have led to confusion was failure to distinguish between perceptual and physical space. Perceptual space consists of perceptual relations between parts of percepts, whereas physical space consists of inferred relations between inferred physical things. What I see may be outside my percept of my body, but not outside my body as a physical thing.

Philosophical discussions on perception are inevitably concerned with two different aspects of the question. George[4] in a recent paper says: 'We know all we know from appearances, and we make, as the basis of these appearances, just whatever assumptions are necessary to make appearances consistent, and that is precisely the job of empirical science. . . . There are problems of lan-

guage and problems of empirical fact and our job is to
investigate the two together.' Perhaps both 'assumptions'
and 'making appearances consistent' could be criticized
in this passage. But there can be no doubt that there are
empirical facts about perception to be known and to be
described in language. Philosophers, it seems to me, are
often ignorant of, or take too limited a view of, important
empirical facts, while scientists are apt to be content with
too simple a description of them. As a neurologist I propose to begin by giving an account of some of the empirical facts.

The neurologist observes the brains of animals and of
other people. From the behaviour of both and from the
answers which patients give to his questions, he discovers
that, when an object is perceived, a series of events occurs
successively in time, beginning with an event in the object
and ending with an event in the subject's brain. If the series
is interrupted at any point between the object and the
cerebral cortex (brain surface) of the subject, the object is
not perceived. If the relevant area of the cortex is destroyed,
the object again is not perceived. But if the relevant area
of the cortex is electrically stimulated while the subject is
conscious, sense-data of a kind aroused by an object are
perceived by the subject. Thus it is held that the event immediately preceding, or perhaps synchronous with, the perception of an object is an event of a physico-chemical kind in
the subject's cerebral cortex. The cortical neurones are normally excited in the way just described from the external
world, but if they should exceptionally be excited in some
other way—for example by electrical stimulation or by an
epileptic discharge—the appropriate sense-data would still be
experienced. The only independently necessary condition for
the awareness of sense-data, to use Broad's term, is thus an
event in the cerebral cortex.[5]

This is an account of the pathways by which sensory impulses travel within the nervous system: what of these impulses themselves? The difference in pitch of two sounds is correlated with a difference in the frequencies of the corresponding vibrations in the air, but no such difference is to be found in the events in the nervous system upon which the discrimination of the two sounds as sensory events depends. These have neither the frequency of the stimuli, nor do they differ from each other in frequency. They differ only in that the nervous impulses travel by different paths and reach different destinations in the cerebral cortex; and this seems to be true not only of the difference between one sound and another, but also of the differences between the nervous impulses underlying our awareness of sounds, sights, and smells. As Adrian[6] says: 'The quality of the sensation seems to depend on the path which the impulses must travel, for apart from this there is little to distinguish the messages from different receptors.'

What I have just been giving you is a scientific account of what goes on in the nervous system when we perceive something. Such things as nerve-impulses and physico-chemical changes cannot themselves be seen: they are inferences from the appearances which the scientist observes in the course of his experiments. It is not necessary to decide the philosophical status of scientific concepts in order to believe that these ideas correspond to something objective, and for everyday purposes philosophers are ready to act as if established scientific 'facts' were true. The philosopher does not knowingly drink a glass of poison on the ground that it looks and tastes like water: he accepts the scientist's account of it. In particular it is generally agreed that if the account which science gives of two events or objects is different, the events or objects are different. Science says that what characterizes a red object is the emission or reflection of light of a certain wave-length and frequency, and what characterizes a string sounding middle C is a vibration of a certain frequency, but it adds that, though each of these states of the object causes distinctive changes in the nervous system of the person seeing red or hearing middle C, these nervous changes, which are the physical basis and only independently necessary condition of seeing red or hearing middle C, are quite unlike the states of the objects seen or heard.

This is one of the empirical bases of the sense-datum theory of perception. Though in fundamentals this view goes back to Descartes, Locke, Berkeley, and Hume, the term 'sense-data' appears to have been coined by Bertrand Russell[7] in 1912 when he wrote: 'Let us give the name of "sense-data" to the things that are immediately known in sensation: such things as colours, sounds, smells, hardnesses, roughnesses, and so on. We shall give the name "sensation" to the experience of being immediately aware of these things.' I propose in my second lecture to deal with philosophical criticisms of the sense-datum theory.

I shall now confine myself to the neurological aspects of the subject, which are three. First, neurology contributes to the scientific account of normal perception. Secondly, the neurologist and the psychiatrist see many people who experience illusions and hallucinations. They have therefore exceptional knowledge of how such people describe and react to their experiences, and whether these are like or unlike normal acts of perception. Finally, the neurologist studies the way in which illusions and hallucinations are produced by disturbances of the nervous system, and how they fit into a general conception of the part played by the brain in perception.

I have already set out the evidence that the sensory qualities of normal perception, such as colours, sounds, smells, and touches, are generated by the brain of the percipient and are unlike those external events which constitute the states of objects by which they are caused. Whatever may be the relation of such sense-data to objects other than the brain, they cannot therefore be parts of such objects or identical with them.

Now let us turn to such abnormal experiences as illusions and hallucinations. These phenomena are relevant to the sense-datum theory of perception, because if having an hallucination to which no object corresponds is a sensory experience in itself indistinguishable from seeing a real object, this is a strong argument for the view that seeing a real object also involves experiencing a sense-datum which is generated by the brain and is therefore independent of the object. Some philosophers, as we shall see, have devoted much ingenuity to providing different descriptions of these two experiences, but the problem is not primarily a semantic but an empirical one. We must therefore begin by finding out what these experiences are and how those who experience them describe and regard them.

I shall begin by giving a fairly detailed description of the phenomena which both parties to the philosophical dispute are seeking to interpret. This is all the more important because it is evident that most philosophers who discuss the nature of hallucinations have had no personal experience of them. I do not mean by that merely that they themselves have never been hallucinated, but that they seem not to have had the opportunity of discussing hallucinations with those who have experienced them, nor even, to judge from their writings, to have read the accounts given by the subjects of hallucinations.

I shall leave on one side for the present what may be termed everyday illusions, for example, the oval appearance of a penny seen from an angle and the colour of distant hills, which are much discussed in philosophical arguments about perception. These are experiences which no doubt must find an interpretation in any theory of perception, but they are common to all of us, and if a philosopher gives a wrong account of them this can easily be detected. That, however, is not the case with all other types of perceptual experience, some normal and others abnormal. Some such experiences cannot be fully described, or properly interpreted, without training of a special kind which most philosophers lack.

I shall begin by describing some common visual experiences, and then turn to the illusions and hallucinations produced by drugs and disease of the nervous system. In doing so I shall use the word 'see' as it is actually used by those who describe these experiences. I shall leave for subsequent discussion whether in such circumstances the word 'see' is rightly used.

There are different kinds of visual after-image, but one will be sufficient for our present purpose. Hanging on the wall opposite me is a picture with a black frame. I look at it steadily for a few seconds, and then without closing my eyes look to one side. I now see against the wall a white rectangle, which is the same shape and size as the picture frame, but is white instead of black. This white rectangle lasts for a few seconds before fading away. While it lasts, if I either turn my eyes without turning my head, or turn my head and my eyes at the same time, I see the white rectangle in a different position in relation to the opposite wall, namely, in the direction in which I am at the time looking. Furthermore, if I tilt my head, the white rectangle also becomes tilted and is now seen at an angle to the black picture frame. Finally, if during the experience of the white rectangle I close my eyes I continue to see it, and if I then move my head, the white rectangle is again seen in a different position in relation to the position of my body, but no longer in relation to my visual experience of the wall opposite, since, my eyes being closed, I have none.

Now let us turn to some accounts of visual hallucinations. The following quotations are taken from the account of his experiences given by a man who had taken lysergic acid.[8]

Then my attention became preoccupied with the dull, gold stars on the lamp shade. These stars began to be filled with colour; they *lived* with colour. One star, I now saw, was a very small (and wholly attractive) *turtle* on its back, its body a maze of distinct colours—the colours which must actually be involved in the gold paint itself. These little turtles—stars —or highwaymen with two huge pistols!—lived and moved in their firmament of illumined paper. . . . Then my eyes went to the whitish-gold distempered wall above, where the lamp-light fell. The wall began to be covered with an incredibly beautiful series of patterns—embossed, drawn, painted, but *continuously changing*. More colour. Indescribable colour. And all the colours, all the patterns, *were in the wall* in any case—only we don't usually see them, for we haven't eyes to. . . . Looking at my bright blue pyjamas on the bed eight feet away, I saw that the blue was *edged with flame*: a narrow flickering, shifting nimbus, incredibly beautiful, which it filled me with delight to watch. Clear flame; golden-scarlet. Then I understood that this flame *was music*, that I was *seeing sound*.

Here is the account given by another observer of his experience under the influence of mescaline.[9]

I received two subcutaneous injections between nine and ten in the morning. . . . At about 11 a.m. changes in the *colour* of objects were noted and the increased intensity of after-images became disturbing. With closed eyes visions of moving constantly changing patterns appeared and attracted the whole attention. Oriental tapestry, mosaic-like wall-papers, kaleidoscopic-coloured geometric patterns, lines in brilliant luminescent colours or in black and white, etc. . . . The colours of real objects appeared more pure, more clean, untarnished by dirt. . . . There were also visual hallucinations unconnected with my conscious thinking, especially friendly animals, little demons and dwarfs, fairy-tale ornaments and mythology from the aquarium such as one sees sometimes on the walls of inns. The faces of people around me were slightly distorted as if drawn by a cartoonist, often with the emphasis on some small, humorous, but, nevertheless, rather characteristic feature.

Writers on the philosophical aspects of perception rarely concern themselves with illusions or hallucinations involving any other sense than vision, but if we are to learn about the status of hallucinations in general this is unduly restricting, and may be actually misleading, if there turn out to be certain features peculiar to hallucinations in the sphere of vision which, in the absence of information about other forms of hallucinations, might be taken to be characteristic of hallucinations in general. Let me, therefore, now describe the experiences of two patients who suffered from hallucinations of smell. One experienced what he described as 'a smell of rubber burning' which would last for hours at a time. He said: 'I would wake up at night and smell burning, and I woke my wife and said there is something on fire—and I'd heard of a beam in those old farmhouses smouldering for days. And then', he went on, 'I realized it wasn't the house that was on fire—it was me!' I asked him how he discovered this, and he replied: 'Well, when I went some-where else and found I could still smell it.' Another patient had her first attack of hallucination of smell while driving her car. Thinking the car battery was leaking she stopped the car to look at it. And here is the account which another patient gave me of her experience of a buzzing in the ears. 'It sounded like the bombers coming over during the war. It was a long time before I found out it was me.'

Disease of the brain may produce illusions and halluci-nations over the whole range of sensory experience which do not differ in character from those which can be pro-duced by the administration of drugs. Let me now quote a few examples of illusions and hallucinations occurring as part of the manifestations of an epileptic attack or elicited by electrical stimulation of the brain in the fully conscious patient.[10] First, here is an account of a visual illusion as part of an epileptic attack recorded by his doctor. 'While I was visiting him this evening the patient said: "Wait a minute! You are getting bigger. The nurse is standing beside you. She is getting bigger. Watch me!" I asked, "Are you having an attack now?" No reply.' Then follows a description of the attack. And here is an account of an hallucination of hearing.

In these later attacks, she heard voices which seemed to be coming from her right. They were not the voices of her children. Indeed she said she could not hear her children speak to her during an attack. Once, on getting up at night to go to the bathroom, she heard music. She thought it came from the radio in the living room. It was a song she had frequently heard on the radio. She could not hear the words.

Another patient said that she would hear music at the beginning of her seizure 'and the music was always the same, a lullaby her mother had sung, "Hushabye my baby"'. When this patient's brain was stimulated she said 'I hear people coming in, I hear music now, a funny little piece'. Stimulation was continued. She became more talkative than usual, explaining that the music was something she had heard on the radio, that it was the theme song of a children's programme.

Now consider some illusions and hallucinations arising in connexion with awareness of the body. The simplest and commonest of these is the 'phantom limb', which is the name for the persistent feeling of the presence of a limb which has been amputated. Phantom limbs must have been known to humanity ever since injury or warfare led to the loss of a part of the body. This strange experience is not limited to limbs, but can apply to many parts, including the nose or a tooth. The phenomenon interested Descartes, and Nelson, after losing his arm, had a phantom one, which for some reason he regarded as a proof of the existence of the soul. Of course a phantom limb can only be felt and not seen, but the feeling may be so convincing that a man who has a phantom leg may fall down because he attempts to stand on it. The subject may feel that he is able to move his phantom limb, and it may be the site of severe and persistent pain. In most cases a painless phantom limb gradually shortens and after a time disappears into the amputation stump.

But amputation is not the only cause of phantom limbs. If certain sensory nerve-paths between a normal limb and the brain are interrupted the patient may feel that he has a second limb in a different place from the real one. Suppose this happens in the case of an arm. Since the interruption of the nerve-paths takes away the feeling from his arm, he now says that he has one arm which he can see, but not feel, and another arm which he can feel, but not see.

Drugs which cause hallucinations may produce the most bizarre effects upon the subject's awareness of his body. One who had taken mescaline said: 'I felt my body particularly plastic and minutely carved. At once I had a sensation as if my foot was being taken off. Then I felt as if my head had been turned by 180 degrees. . . . My feet turned spirals and scrolls, my jaw was like a hook and my chest seemed to melt away.'[11] Not only may the body feel enlarged; it may enter into a complicated scene. One subject, also under mescaline and lying with his arms crossed, said: 'My right arm is a street with a group of toy soldiers. My left arm goes across the street like a bridge and carries a railway.'[12]

To complete this account of the perceptual changes produced by mescaline intoxication I must mention the occurrence of synaesthesiae, that is the irradiation of sensation from one sense to another. For example, one subject found that the colours of his visual hallucinations were altered by changes in the rhythm of the music being played on the radio. Mayer-Gross[9] quotes an experience of a subject under mescaline which illustrates what he calls not only 'the peculiar result of the synaesthetic perception, but also the inadequacy of ordinary language for such experiences'. 'What I see, I hear; what I smell,

I think. I am music, I am the lattice-work. I see an idea of mine going out of me into the lattice-work. . . . I felt, saw, tasted and smelled the noise of the trumpet, was myself the noise. . . . Everything was clear and absolutely certain. All criticism is nonsense in the face of experience.'

But lest it be thought that these results of the administration of drugs are quite remote from the experiences of normal people, let me quote Grey Walter's[13] observations on the effect of exposing normal individuals to a flickering light. At certain frequencies around ten per second some subjects see whirling spirals, whirlpools, explosions, Catherine wheels which do not correspond to any causal physical event. There may be organized hallucinations, and all sorts of emotions are experienced. Sometimes the sense of time is lost or disturbed. One subject said that he had been 'pushed sideways in time'—yesterday was at one side, instead of behind, and tomorrow was off the port bow.

If I am to give a comprehensive account of hallucinations, that is to provide all the data which a philosophical explanation of them needs to take into account, there are some further points which I must add. An hallucination may be present to one sense, but not to another, as in the case of a phantom limb. Perhaps the best-known example of this is Macbeth's dagger.

Is this a dagger which I see before me
The handle toward my hand? Come, let me clutch thee.
I have thee not, and yet I see thee still.
Art thou not, fatal vision, sensible
To feeling as to sight? or art thou but
A dagger of the mind, a false creation,
Proceeding from the heat-oppressed brain?

Similar experiences are common in psychiatry. On the

other hand an hallucination may be present to more than one sense. For example, a person may think that he sees a coin on the floor. He may then stoop and pick up the hallucinatory coin and say that he can feel its milled edge with his finger. Or he may say that he sees a human figure and that the figure speaks to him, and he can hear its words. Probably the most elaborate hallucinatory experiences are those of so-called apparitions. Smythies[14] gives an excellent summary of the characteristics of these hallucinations. He says:

The hallucinated object or person purports to be a physical object—i.e. it looks and behaves very like a physical object or person. And 'an apparition' usually looks solid, throws a proper shadow, gets smaller as it moves away from the observer, moves around the room with respect of the furniture, gets dimmer as it moves into the more dimly lit parts of the room, may speak to the observer or even touch him. In nearly one half of the reported cases the 'apparition' has been seen by more than one observer at the same time—i.e. there are collective hallucinations. These features of this class of hallucinations may be summarized by stating that the internal and external organization of the hallucination *approaches* that of veridical perception. An 'apparition' may be so 'life-like' as to be frequently confused with the biological person it purports to be. They frequently satisfy the criteria by which we judge what is and what is not a veridical perception and are accepted as members of the class of veridical perceptions—at any rate for a time—although this membership is usually cancelled by subsequent experience, as when the apparition suddenly disappears or information is later obtained that the person hallucinated was actually at that time in a distant part of the country.

I have given a by no means exhaustive account of the rich variety of hallucinatory experiences, but I have

described enough to be able to draw attention to certain
points. First, no hard-and-fast line can be drawn intro-
spectively between normal perception, illusions, and hallucinations. The subject under the influence of mescaline
or lysergic acid describes modifications in the appearance
of the objects around him. 'The wall began to be covered
with an incredibly beautiful series of patterns.' 'Looking
at my bright blue pyjamas . . . I saw that the blue was
edged with flame.' 'The colours of real objects appeared
more fine.' 'The faces of people around me were slightly
distorted.' These experiences merge into others in which
the change involves the nature of the object itself. 'These
stars [on the lampshade] began to be filled with colour . . .
the star, I now saw, was a very small (and wholly attractive) turtle. . . . These little turtles—stars—or highwaymen with two huge pistols!—lived and moved in their
firmament of illumined paper.' From this a step takes us
to visual hallucinations which seem independent of any
object in the environment—animals, demons, and dwarfs,
for example—and finally to 'visions' of coloured patterns
seen with closed eyes.

Secondly, in describing illusions and hallucinations the
subjects, whether normal or abnormal, frequently use the
words 'see', 'hear', and 'smell', and not the phrases 'seem
to see', 'seem to hear', and 'seem to smell'. When I am
describing my own experience of visual after-images it
seems natural to say that I see them. I do not mean by
that that I believe that I am seeing any physical object,
but that the after-images have a sensory quality in common with the seeing of the object which has immediately
preceded them, that they are describable in similar terms
in respect of colour and spatial extension, and moreover
they have some relationship to my eyes since they move

when I move my eyes. Similarly the patient who had a visual illusion in an epileptic attack did not say: 'You seem to be growing bigger', but 'You are growing bigger'. Thus the patient describing an illusion often uses the same terms with which he describes the reality. He does not discriminate the illusion as a sensory experience from the reality as a sensory experience, and he describes both in the same way. How, then, does he distinguish between them when he does so? By reasoning. He compares the appearance or behaviour of the illusory object with what he knows is its normal appearance or behaviour, and concludes that he is experiencing an illusion.

Thirdly, both the drug-induced illusions and the hallucinatory 'apparitions' show that these abnormal experiences are often associated with a modification of normal perception such that the abnormal appearance is integrated into the subject's perception of his environment. When an apparition hides from view an object in front of which it is standing, or opens and passes through a door known to be locked, it provides the strongest evidence that the sense-data comprising the apparition and those comprising the environment possess the same perceptual status, and that those events, whatever they may be, which are causing the subject to see the apparition are at the same time appropriately modifying his perception of the rest of his environment. Perhaps I should add at this point that I am concerned with these phenomena purely as hallucinations and express no views as to the epistemological status of apparitions.

Now although there are many hallucinatory states which present themselves with the same sensory vividness as veridical perceptions, and of which the subject naturally, and in my view appropriately, says 'I see', 'I

hear', or 'I smell' so-and-so, there are other experiences
which are usually and appropriately described by the
subject with the words 'I seemed to see', 'I seemed to
hear', or 'I seemed to smell'. The commonest example of
this is a dream. If we relate our dreams, we commonly
do so in some such words as Bottom's: 'Methought I
was,—and methought I had,—'. Our account of our
dreams is usually retrospective, though I do not know
whether philosophers in their dreams give themselves an
account of their experiences. But although in our dreams
most of us have experiences which we describe in visual
terms—and in what other terms could we discuss, for
example, whether an object seen in a dream is coloured
or not?—we do, looking back on a dream in memory,
regard it as having a sensory quality which distinguishes
it from a waking experience. And the same applies to
visual imagery and visual memory in a subject who has
these faculties strongly developed. However vividly he
may see an object in his memory or in his imagination
he is never likely to make the mistake of thinking he is
seeing it in reality: he will recognize that he is seeing it
in his 'mind's eye'. No doubt the perceptual character of
the experience is only one reason for this: the subject
knows that he is himself responsible for remembering, or
for imagining, in a way in which he is not responsible
for the appearance of things he perceives or his hallucinations. However, there are disorders of sleep in which the
subject, who may be described as half-awake, fails to
distinguish between the events of his dream and the
reality of his environment which he also perceives. He
may then, as it were, act out his dream in his ordinary
surroundings. This, though rare in adults, is by no means
uncommon in a child awakening from a nightmare. In

some mental disorders, too, the patient's phantasies may not have the vivid perceptual external location of hallucinations, but rather the quality of dreams or imagination mingling with the everyday environment. Thus, while there are many perceptual experiences in which a hallucination has sensory qualities indistinguishable to the subject from veridical perceptual experiences and which are naturally, and appropriately, described in the same terms, there are also both normal and abnormal mental states in which images may play a part which are not naturally or appropriately so described.

This is not the occasion on which to discuss in detail how disorder of the function of the brain produces illusions and hallucinations, but there is one simple point, which is illustrated by the common experience of an attack of migraine. Here a disturbance of the part of the brain concerned with seeing often causes the subject to see scintillating and coloured patterns extending over an area of the visual field and in that area replacing normal vision. The disordered brain state is producing abnormal visual sense-data which take their place among the remaining normal ones and are seen in a situation which can be explained in terms of the anatomy of the nervous system.

Before I leave the subject of hallucinations I must briefly consider the argument sometimes put forward by philosophers, for example by Hirst,[15] that we are not entitled to draw inferences about normal perception from hallucinations because the subject of hallucinations is not in a normal mental state. Hirst writes:

It is characteristic of such hallucinations that the victim is not in full control of his faculties and powers of discrimination owing to drunkenness, fever, madness, starvation, or even acute anxiety or drowsiness. Hence he is not able to distinguish properly between perceived objects or mental or dream images, especially as, owing to these disposing factors, the images often have unusual vividness. . . . The victim of such hallucinations is not in a normal state; we must, therefore, challenge the belief that having hallucinations is normal sensing or perceiving but with a peculiar sort of object.

The last sentence of this quotation raises a semantic question to which I shall return later, but Hirst's contention, that the abnormal state of the subject of hallucinations invalidates the inference which exponents of the sense-datum theory draw from them, is itself invalid. Smythies[16] has dealt with Hirst's objection. It should be clear from the examples I have given that although hallucinations are in themselves abnormal, since people do not normally experience them, the subject of hallucinations is not necessarily in a state in which he is unable to recognize or accurately describe the nature of his experience. Havelock Ellis, quoted by Smythies, writes: 'The mescal drinker remains calm and collected amid the sensory turmoil around him; his judgment is as clear as in the normal state.' My patient with the hallucination of smell, who thought that his house was burning, was in all respects normal apart from the fact that he was having an hallucination. As Smythies says: 'Confusion and hallucination are thus clearly two independent variables, which though often found together, are nevertheless to be found apart.' To suppose that the mere fact of having hallucinations makes the subject's account of them unreliable is to beg the question.

Let me summarize this lecture by saying that the facts of physics and physiology show that perception is the end-result of a series of physical events, the last of which, a state of activity of the brain of the percipient, differs so completely from the events occurring in the object perceived that the qualitative features of a percept can have no resemblance to the physical object which it represents. The perceptual world, therefore, if I may use the term to describe the whole realm of our perceptual experience, is a construct of the percipient's brain. When, as the result of disordered function of his brain, he experiences hallucinations, these have the same sensory characteristics as veridical percepts, and in some instances such hallucinations are integrated into their perceptual environment, which is reciprocally modified. These and similar facts form the empirical basis of the sense-datum theory. In my next lecture I shall be discussing the views of some philosophers who disagree with it, and some of its implications.

II

THE NATURE OF PERCEPTION

In my first lecture I set out some of the more important empirical grounds for believing that the sensory qualities of the objects which we perceive are constructed by the activity of our own brains, which are thus responsible for producing what have been called sense-data. Before I consider some of the wider implications of this view I must deal with the main objections to it raised by some philosophers. These can be found elaborated in the writings of Ryle,[17, 18] Paul,[19] Hirst,[15] Flew,[20] Lean,[21] Quinton,[22] Ayer,[23] and George,[4] to mention some recent writers. Since they all cover much the same ground the simplest plan seems to be to classify their principal arguments, quoting when necessary from particular authors.

1. Ayer[23] says of the 'contention that we directly perceive sense-data rather than physical objects' that 'whether true or false, it is not an empirical statement of fact. A philosopher who thinks that he directly perceives physical objects does not for that reason expect anything different to happen from what is expected by one who believes that he directly perceives sense-data.' Lean[21] puts the same point somewhat differently when he says that 'in perceiving a chair the very first visual experience we have is of the chair. . . . Dr. Broad must be mistaken in holding that sensations play an indispensable part in perceptual situations. They play no part at all.'

2. Ryle[18] attacks the causal theory of perception. 'There is something drastically wrong', he writes, 'with the whole programme of trying to schedule my seeing a tree either as a physiological or as a psychological end-stage of processes. . . . To put the point much too crudely, seeing a tree is not an effect—but this is not because it is an eccentric sort of state or process which happens to be exempt from causal explanations, but because it is not a state or process at all.' He concludes that 'a certain kind of dilemma about perception' arises because 'from some well-known facts of optics, acoustics and physiology it seemed to follow that what we see, hear or smell cannot be, as we ordinarily suppose, things and happenings outside us, but are on the contrary things or happenings inside us'. A modification of the latter part of this argument is put forward by Ayer, Lean, and Flew, who argue that the fact that our percepts are causally determined by various external circumstances does not mean that we have no direct knowledge of physical objects.

3. Lean[21] argues that

from the fact that there are delusive perceptual situations whose epistemological objects do not correspond to any ontological object in the external world, and from the added fact that there is no 'relevant difference' between delusive and veridical perceptual situations, it is obvious that all Dr. Broad is entitled to conclude reasonably is that in no case can one know from a given perceptual situation alone whether or not it contains as a constituent the physical object which corresponds to its epistemological object. This of course is quite a different matter from concluding that in no case does a perceptual situation contain such an object as its constituent.

Ryle's version of this argument is that perceptual errors

imply veridical perceptions in the same way that false coins imply the existence of true coins.

4. Philosophers who do not accept the sense-datum theory are compelled to maintain that hallucinations differ in some recognizable respect from normal perceptions apart from their failure to represent physical objects. Thus, Lean says that 'we may only in an analogous and purely grammatical sense speak of the "objects" of our hallucinatory experiences'. The sense-data which Broad calls 'epistemological objects' Lean describes as 'the visual sensation itself hypostatized into a kind of entity'. Ayer, speaking of Macbeth's visionary dagger, says: 'It is only if we artificially combine the decision to say that the victim of a hallucination is seeing something with the ruling that what is seen must exist, that we secure the introduction of sense-data. But once again there seems to be no good reason why we should do this.' While it may be legitimate to say that Macbeth seems to see a dagger, what follows from this? Ayer summarizes his criticism by saying: 'What appears most dubious of all is the final step by which we are to pass from "it seems to me that I perceive X" to "I perceive a seeming-X", with the implication that there is a seeming-X which I perceive.'

5. I turn now to two arguments of a more general kind. The first concerns the time-element in perception, which is stressed by Russell. Since all transmission of physical energy takes time, and all perception depends upon physical energy transmitting light waves and sound waves to the body and nervous impulses within it, and since we do not perceive any object until the relevant nervous impulses reach the brain, our perception must always be later than the state of the object which it

represents, only a fraction of a second later when the object is a piece of wool touching the skin, eight minutes later when the object is the sun, and many thousands of years later when the object is a distant star. Few philosophers concern themselves with this argument, but Ayer deals with it as follows. He says:

> It is assumed that, unlike our memories or our imaginations, our eyes cannot range into the past; whatever it is that we see must exist here and now if it exists at all. But this assumption is not unassailable. Why should it not be admitted that our eyes can range into the past, if all that is meant by this is that the time at which we see things may be later than the time when they are in the states in which we see them?

6. Finally, there is the criticism, which has been often expressed, that the sense-datum view of perception is self-contradictory. Let me quote part of Hirst's[15] summary of this mode of attack.

> If we, as minds, never directly perceive material objects but are only directly aware of images or mental representations allegedly caused by them, how do we know that there are any material or physical causes or what their nature is? We cannot look behind the barrier of ideas to see what their causes are like, if they have any. Locke . . . failed to notice that his theory is self-refuting, for its conclusion contradicts the premise assumed in physiology that we do perceive material things such as sense organs and brains.

The first four groups of argument which I have just summarized are all based upon a rejection of the causal view of perception. This rejection is most openly stated by Ryle when he says: 'To put the point much too crudely, seeing a tree is not an effect—but this is not because it is an eccentric sort of state or process which happens to be exempt from causal explanations, but because it is not a state or process at all.' What Ryle is saying here is, first, that seeing a tree is not a state or process, and secondly because it is not a state or process it is not an effect. When he says that seeing a tree is not a state or process he is presumably alluding to seeing a tree as an experience of the percipient, and probably we should all agree that when we see a tree we do not normally describe it as a state or process, nor do we regard it as an effect. But that is because in order to be aware of something as an effect we must know it as occurring at the end of a causal series of events. But the series of events which ends in perception is never given to the introspection of the percipient. Hence as long as I confine my observations to my own world of perceptions I can never discover that seeing a tree *is* an effect. When, however, I observe someone else seeing a tree, and take into account all the relevant scientific facts in physics and physiology, I find that although the subject of the observation may not regard his seeing a tree as an effect, a state, or a process, its causation can be fairly exactly described in scientific terms, and the scientific explanation shows that when he sees a tree he is experiencing sense-data which are the effects of a long chain of causation ending in his brain, and in important respects are unlike the tree as a physical object. It follows that the causal nature of seeing cannot be discovered by introspection, and that there are important arguments for the existence of sense-data which introspection cannot refute. This appears to be what Ayer means when he says that: 'Whether true or false, [the contention that we directly see sense-data] is not an empirical statement of fact', if by 'empirical' he here means open to introspection. Hence, if it is true that 'a philosopher who thinks that he directly perceives physical objects does not for that reason expect anything different to happen from what is expected by one who believes that he directly perceives sense-data', this statement is true but irrelevant. This applies also to Lean's statement that sense-data play no part in the process of perceiving a chair.

The same philosophers attack the causal theory of perception in another way. Ryle says: 'A certain kind of dilemma about perception' arises because 'from some well-known facts of optics, acoustics and physiology it seemed to follow that what we see, hear or smell cannot be, as we ordinarily suppose, things and happenings outside us, but are on the contrary things or happenings inside us.' Other philosophers argue that the fact that our perceptions are causally influenced by conditions outside ourselves, as well as by our own nervous systems, does not mean that they do not give us direct knowledge of external objects. This view seems to rest on a confusion of thought. When such a philosopher needs spectacles he does not, I imagine, say that the oculist cannot help him because, in Ryle's words, 'seeing a tree is not an effect'; he accepts the fact that his faulty vision is an effect, and that his seeing a tree can be improved if he is given glasses to correct the errors in his own eyes. He accepts the causal theory up to a point, because it is clear that his visual perceptions are influenced by distance, the light, the state of the atmosphere, and his own refractive errors. He would no doubt go farther and accept the fact that vision can be modified for the worse by diseases of the relevant parts of the nervous system. But he appears to regard all these causal influences as operating upon a normal state of affairs which itself is not causally determined. He thus mixes his introspectionist view of perception with an incomplete version of the causal theory, including only those causal factors of which his direct perception makes him aware. The complete scientific view of perception affords no empirical or logical basis for the idea that there is an irreducible given element, namely, direct awareness of objects, which is both independent of, and yet can be causally affected by, events which can be described in terms of physics and physiology.

Ryle's statement that 'from some well-known facts of optics, acoustics and physiology it seemed to follow that what we see, hear or smell cannot be, as we ordinarily suppose, things and happenings outside us, but are on the contrary things or happenings inside us' arises from a confusion between physical and perceptual space. This distinction is fundamental to the sense-datum theory, and is relevant to the two more general questions to which I drew attention, namely, the space–time relationship in perception and the realists' objection that if we know only sense-data we cannot know anything of their causes. At this point, therefore, I shall turn from criticizing the critics to a statement of the views about perception which I hold.

If we start our description of perceptual knowledge with a subject and an object we shall rapidly get into difficulties from which there is no escape. The fact with which we must begin is the fact of knowledge, experience, or information, if we use the last word, as I think we must, to imply a receiver as well as something received. If we start with knowledge or experience we start with the subject–object relationship already given. We do not need to ask how we become aware of things outside ourselves because it is with that awareness that we begin. It is easy to fall into the error of supposing that the sense-data generated by the brain must be *entirely* unlike the physical objects which, by acting upon the brain from the outside world, produce them. But, with some important exceptions, this view is mistaken. The human brain is the climax of millions of years of evolutionary selection of the capacity to react to the physical environment in an ever more complex manner. On the receptive side this depends upon a progressive increase in the powers of discrimination of certain sense-organs, especially the eyes, while the brain has developed *pari passu* the ability to utilize this increasingly varied and complex information for the purposes of action. Thus, as I have said elsewhere,

the receptive function of the cerebral cortex is to provide us with a symbolical representation of the whole of the external world, not only distinguishing objects by their qualities, but also conveying to us the spatial relationships which exist between them, and at the same time giving us similar symbolical information about our own bodies and their relationship with the external world. All this information, of course, is given us not merely for the sake of pure awareness or contemplation, though that may sometimes be a by-product of it, but in order that we may act; hence it is linked, in ways with which we are familiar, with the motor activities of the brain.[5]

Thus, one of the most important functions of the brain is to provide us with an accurate representation of the spatial structure of the external world as well as of our own bodies. An important part of this structure is the ever-changing relationship between our bodies and their environment: awareness of the externality of what is outside our bodies is therefore given in all ordinary acts of sense perception.

What follows from this? First, that our perception of external objects is orientated in relation to the position of our own body: it is a perspective, as Russell uses the term. This has many implications. Neurology tells us that our awareness of the spatial relations of objects is extremely complex and is the outcome of contributions from many sources, including our own bodies, some of which are not recognized as such. Moreover, our awareness of the spatial relations of objects is never limited to perceptions of the objects themselves: it is imbued with past experiences of movement and time, so that my awareness of a book on a table, as it were, sketches out in advance the movements necessary in order to reach it and pick it up. And an object seen is seen endowed with those qualities which experience has shown it to have for other sensory modalities, tactile shape, texture, temperature, weight, &c.

All knowledge is both subjective and objective, or it would not be knowledge. The objective features are the information which it gives about the external object; the subjective features those which make it *my* knowledge, namely, its relationship to my other past and present experiences, and any contribution which my brain may make to the representation of the object.

Although the brain has a highly developed capacity for reproducing the structure of the external world, those of its states which cause us to experience colours, sounds, and smells cannot, as we have seen earlier, be like the physical features of the objects which evoke these sensory qualities. Sense-data therefore cannot be transmitted from physical objects: they must be engendered by the brain

B 7390   D

itself. Let us consider colour. Most animals are colour-blind. We have only to compare a coloured photograph with one in black and white to appreciate the great increase in the power of discrimination of objects which has resulted from the evolution of the power to appreciate colour. Awareness of structure implies awareness of something which possesses that structure. The brain in order to develop its powers of discrimination had to sacrifice the direct response to physical stimuli which the unicellular organism possesses. This devolved upon specific sense-organs, such as the eye, which responded by transmitting to the brain not the original physical stimuli, but physiological impulses. The eye having acquired the power to discriminate the different wave-lengths of light which underlie colour-perception, the brain responded by producing the sensory qualities which we call colours. When, therefore, we are aware of objects around us by vision we see them labelled by the brain, as it were, with colours. As Whitehead[24] puts it:

the true doctrine of sense-perception is that the qualitative characters of affective tones inherent in the bodily functionings are transmuted into the characters of regions. These regions are then perceived as associated with those character-qualities, but also these same qualities are shared by the subjective forms of the prehensions.

I spoke earlier of the brain providing us with 'a symbolical representation of the whole of the external world'. In so far as sensory qualities are contributed by the brain they may be regarded as symbolical representations of the physical properties of objects which the brain is incapable of representing in any other way.

The objects about which I have been speaking are the objects around us with which we are all familiar, things we see and hear and feel, tables and books and our own bodies. Each of us is aware of them as existing in space, and in that space a table or a book is outside the body of the observer. In terms of this space the table is object and the observer is subject, the observer for this purpose being identified with his body. The scientific account of perception, however, teaches us that the objects which we perceive outside our bodies are not as independent of us as they appear to be: they have qualities which are generated by our brains and which have no other existence. Nevertheless we do not believe that books and tables are objects entirely generated by our brains. Since other people are aware of them, and since they continue to exist when no one is aware of them, we infer that they have an independent existence of some kind. If we call the things which go on existing, whether we perceive them or not, physical objects, and the things which we perceive, perceptual objects, we are faced with the question of the relationship between them. If we reject, as science shows us we must, the realist view of perception held by the introspectionist philosophers, it becomes clear that there are important differences between physical objects and perceptual objects. In particular, if the red colour of the book on the table is generated by my brain we must abandon the common-sense realist view of space. There seem to be only two alternative views with which we could replace it. Broad[25] puts the matter as follows:

It seems clear that either (1) sensible determinates (such as some particular shade of red) do not inhere in regions of physical Space–Time, but in regions of some other Space–Time; or (2) that, if they do inhere in regions of physical Space–Time, they must inhere in the latter in some different way from that in which physical determinates (like physical motion) do so. Either there is one sense of 'inherence' and many different Space–Times, or there is one Space–Time and many different senses of 'inherence'.

To put the matter somewhat differently, if there is only one Space–Time it must be such that a sensory quality produced by my brain can exist as a property of an object outside my body. The alternative is to suppose that each of us possesses his own private perceptual space, generated by his brain, in which all his perceptual objects, but not their corresponding physical objects, exist. The concept of a private perceptual space has, I think, the advantages of simplicity and coherence. Let us now see how it explains the facts in competition with the realist view.

The sensory qualities of objects are where they appear to be in the perceptual space of each one of us. Illusions and hallucinations of the kind which I described in my first lecture are the product of alterations in the brain's normal perceptual processes. Since the brain creates the sensory qualities of objects in perceptual space, there is no difficulty in understanding why such illusions and hallucinations should possess the same sensory characteristics as normal perceptual objects and be located, where the subject is aware of them, in his perceptual space.

The realist philosophers who maintain that in normal perception we have direct awareness of objects are compelled to claim that hallucinations have a different perceptual quality from normal objects, so that if a subject says that he 'sees' a visual hallucination, he is wrongly using the word 'see', and should rather say that he 'seems to see' something; and, further, that to say that 'he seems to see an object' is not the same thing as saying that 'he sees a seeming-object'. Their argument runs: seeing requires an object; there is no object corresponding to a visual hallucination; therefore having a visual hallucination is not seeing; therefore it differs perceptually from seeing. This argument is refuted by the experiences of the subject of hallucinations. He describes his experiences by saying, 'I see', 'I hear', or 'I smell', and not 'I seem to see', 'I seem to hear', or 'I seem to smell'; that is to say he does not distinguish the sensory qualities of hallucinations from those of normal perceptions, and this, as we have seen, cannot be attributed to his being in a state of mental confusion. Moreover, no hard-and-fast line can be drawn between visual illusions and visual hallucinations, and when someone who has taken a drug says that he sees his blue pyjamas edged with flame there is no empirical reason for saying that he sees the pyjamas, but that he seems to see the flame. There is, of course, an epistemological distinction between seeing a dagger and seeming to see a dagger, when in the second instance the appearance of the dagger is an hallucination, but this does not imply that the two experiences are perceptually dissimilar. In fact they are not, and it is a semantic question whether it is appropriate to use the word 'see' for the experience of visual sense-data which appear to represent physical objects but do not do so. This question is irrelevant to the question whether sense-data are experienced when an object is seen.

There is one common experience which, it seems to me, only the sense-datum theory of perception will explain. The cinematograph is based upon the fact that a series of still photographs of a moving object taken at an appropriate speed, and projected on to a screen at the same speed, will create for the observer an appearance of movement. What is shown upon the screen is a succession of still pictures; what the observer sees is a 'moving picture'. No ordinary person has any doubt that he sees movement. If it is said that he only seems to see movement we must ask what, that is not movement, resembles movement, and how, except verbally, seeming to see movement differs from seeing movement. And if in fact he sees movement when the physical objects at which he looks do not move, where is the movement that he sees? The answer is that the rapid succession of images on the screen produces in the brain of the observer those changes which normally cause him to experience moving visual sense-data, and the observer consequently sees movement in his perceptual world although there is no corresponding movement in the physical world. A similar effect is produced by the symptom 'oscillopsia' caused by disease of the brain. The patient's eyes involuntarily oscillate, and this causes the stationary objects he sees to appear to move. His sense-data move though the objects they represent do not.

The idea of a private perceptual world belonging to each subject seems also to provide the best solution of the time problem associated with perception. As both Whitehead[24] and Russell[3] have pointed out, owing to the time occupied by the physical processes involved in perception our sense-data must always represent the past state of the object to which they correspond, even when that object is our own body. Ayer replies to this that there is no reason to assume that 'whatever it is that we see must exist here and now if it exists at all. . . . Why should it not be admitted that our eyes can range into the past, if all that is meant by this is that the time at which we see things may be later than the time when they are in the states in which we see them?' But this argument seems to be the result of another illegitimate mixture of the causal and introspectionist views of perception. Direct perceptual experience is of the present, and in itself tells us nothing about the past of objects. It is possible by means of science to infer that my present experience which I call seeing a star gives me information about a long past state of that star in the physical world, but in the physical world no state of an object can be at one and the same time and place both past and present, hence what I now see may represent, but cannot *be*, the past state of the star. What I am conscious of here and now is a sense-datum which exists contemporaneously in my private perceptual space.

For the perceptual world of a single observer possesses not only a space of its own, but also a time of its own, and the time relationships of events in the perceptual world are different from those in the physical world to which they relate. We may generalize this by saying that all events in the perceptual world of a single observer are contemporaneous with the final events in his brain by means of which they are perceived. Amongst other consequences of this state of affairs is the fact that in the perceptual world of a single observer no sense-datum can be the cause of its being perceived, nor of the changes in the nervous system which underlie its perception. The reason is that the coming into existence of the sense-datum, and the neural events concerned in this, are contemporary, and contemporary events cannot enter into a mutual causal relationship. This is the explanation of Ryle's statement, which refers to the perceptual world. that 'seeing is not a process'.

The physical world, therefore, is what we infer about the causes of our perceptions, and since it is a product of inference it is a symbolical representation of the structure of events occurring in space–time. The physical world includes the physical objects to which our perceptual objects refer, and the physical brains by means of which we perceive them. The fact that our perceptual world inevitably always represents a past state of physical objects might seem to interpose a serious gulf between physical objects and our awareness of them, but this is of no practical importance. Our perceptual apparatus was not evolved to deal with objects at astronomical distances, but with the near-by world. So far as vision is concerned the speed of light is so great that the time taken by light waves to travel from any visible terrestrial object to the eye is far too small to be detected by physiological processes with speeds of those which occur in the body. And since the ordinary objects of our perception endure unchanged for periods which are enormously long compared with the time which light takes to travel from them to us, for all practical purposes of perception their past state represented by our present sense-data is identical with their state at the time at which we perceive them. The same applies to the objects which we touch, which do not normally change their state or position in the time which it takes a nerve impulse to pass from the hand to the brain. Perceptual awareness has been evolved to deal with normal conditions, and it is only when the causal conditions of our perceptions become exceptional in respect of space or time that our perceptual knowledge becomes seriously inaccurate.

Where, then, is the perceptual space of each of us? The answer is, in his brain: and this brings us to the point which puzzles so many people, namely, how the colour of the book which I see can be at the same time out there in space and in my brain. The explanation is that when I speak of my brain I naturally think of something I suppose to exist inside the head which I can feel with my hand; but this, even if I could see it by means of mirrors through a hole in my skull, would itself be part of my perceptual world like the book, and, as we have just seen, no event in one person's perceptual world can be the cause of another contemporaneous event in it. My perceptual world, therefore, cannot exist in my perceptual brain: it is in my physical brain that it exists—the brain whose own existence I infer from my perceptual world and the statements of science. This raises many interesting problems with which I have not now time to deal. But in case you have some difficulty in understanding how each of us can have his whole private perceptual space housed in his physical brain, let me illustrate this by what is, I think, a fairly accurate analogy.

A ship's radar consists of a luminous screen not much larger than a dinner-plate. Suppose that you are looking at this screen on a ship sailing in complete darkness some miles offshore from a mountainous island. All that you can see is a luminous plate on which an image of the ship's environment seen in perspective is continuously created and re-created. Away to the port side is the rocky shore of the island with its cliffs and inlets, behind which lie mountains and valleys, their peaks illuminated, and those parts which are hidden from the ship's 'view' lying in shadow, light and shade being represented by different degrees of the yellowish luminosity or by its absence. And as the ship moves onwards the perspective changes, and the unseen light shines into valleys which have been dark before, and throws previously illuminated hills into shadow. And ahead we see the image of a ship sailing

towards us. Here in a minute space in the vast bulk of
the ship is its private perceptual space. The apparatus
contributes its own 'sense-data' in the form of a range of
luminous shades, and by means of these it is able to
reproduce the spatial structure of an environment other-
wise unperceived by the observer. Thus it enables the
captain to take the appropriate action to steer the ship in
relation to the shore and the oncoming ship perceptually
represented. Moreover, in looking at a ship's radar the
observer is at once aware that he is not merely seeing a
picture a foot or so in diameter: he is perceiving through
the apparatus the external world, and through the private
space–time of the screen he is made aware of, and acts
within, the physical space–time, in which the ship itself,
the sea, and the island exist.

In some such fashion I think we should picture perception conveying to us through our private perceptual
worlds knowledge of the physical world in which we live,
and upon which we have to act. And because we start
with the fact of knowledge, experience, or information,
and know that the capacity to provide such information
is inherent in the structure of the brain, however coloured
it necessarily is by its subjectivity, we see that the sense-
datum theory is both logically and empirically compatible
with the view that through our sense-data we do know
about the physical world, which they represent.

Thus there is a complete answer to Hirst[15] and others
who ask how, if perception provides us only with images
or representations of physical objects, we know that
physical objects exist to cause such images or representations. The answer is that awareness of objective elements
is given in perception. Assuming that in general the
number, discreteness, and movement of objects we per-

ceive are objective, science infers a structure of the physical world such that some perceptual elements are shown to be subjective. The self-contradictory view that begins with objects and ends by making them entirely subjective is a misrepresentation of the sense-datum theory.[26]

If objects in my perceptual world are in fact my own creation they can possess not only sensory characteristics, but emotional ones too. This is a process to which the term 'projection' has been applied by the psychoanalysts. Smythies[27] describes it as follows:

In psychoanalytical theory the concept of 'projection' is used primarily to describe the process whereby our own feelings and attitudes, of which we are ashamed or which we find painful and to which we do not wish to admit, are ascribed to others. We come to believe that these other people actually entertain the same feelings towards us and our behaviour is adjusted accordingly.

Projection in the psychoanalytical sense has been defined by Alexander[28] as 'the ascription to the outer world of mental processes that are not recognized to be of personal origin'. Munroe[29] says: 'Owing to the interaction of the mechanisms of introjection and projection, which make the objects part of the self, as it were, external factors come to influence the formation of the personality.' Smythies goes on to say: 'I am not denying that the process referred to by analysts as "projection" may occur exactly as they describe it or that "projection" is a good analogical term for it. But analogical terms can be dangerous and it is better to use literal terms when one can.' He suggests that, in many instances at least, when psychoanalysts speak of the 'projection' of affects, wishes, attitudes, and feelings, the word 'ascription' better expresses what they mean. He points out that the word 'ascription' is actually used in the sentence of Alexander which I have quoted. It may be true that when the psychoanalyst speaks of 'projecting' attitudes and feelings on to other people he merely means that the person who does so is entertaining erroneous beliefs about other people's attitudes and feelings, because he attributes to them attitudes and feelings which they do not in fact possess, but which his own emotional state makes him believe that they do possess. But it seems to me that this process may involve something more than merely an erroneous belief. To believe something about another person, if it is a belief related to that person's feelings and potential behaviour, is to see that person as possessing certain characteristics, and, if the belief is a wrong one, characteristics which he does not possess. It is to make for that person a *persona* which is a false representation of him, and it often involves reacting to the *persona* instead of to the person. This, I would suggest, is no more a process of projection than is our construction of the perceptual world: it is the creation of a *persona* in the world of the imagination—the formation of an image composed of ideas and feelings associated with the perceptual form of the person concerned. What the psychoanalysts call 'projection', therefore, involves the failure to recognize the subjective character of features ascribed to other persons and things.

Though this psychological process has been brought to light and explored by psychoanalysts it is far from confined to those who suffer from psychological disorders: indeed it plays an important part in the mental lives of all of us. Kretschmer[30] discusses what he calls 'the laws of imaginal projection'. 'By imaginal projection', he writes, 'we mean the separation of images into the two main groups—ego and non-ego (outside world).' He points out that the mechanisms of imaginal projection are incompletely developed in primitive man. 'They operate uncertainly—the groups, "ego" and "non-ego" (outside world), "conception" and "perception", are not sharply divided; they overlap in wide and variable border zones. In the child, too, we find this inadequate differentiation of "phantasy" and "reality".' The belief of primitive races in magic and sorcery depends on their failure to draw the line between subjective and objective where it is drawn by civilized man, and even civilized man when he believes in mascots, good and bad luck, and astrology is exhibiting these primitive traits. In this sphere the distinction between an object and the emotion it evokes is by no means clear-cut. In primitive religion and taboos the holy or forbidden object is not analytically regarded as producing feelings of awe or aversion in the subject, but as itself possessing a magical power for good or for evil. In psychoanalysis the concept of a 'father figure' is used to explain how an individual's emotional attitude to his own father may persist to influence subsequently his attitude to persons who in virtue of their age, position of authority, or temperamental characteristics in some way resemble his own father. Neurotic fears of the attitude of other people are often fears, not of how the real people are likely to behave, but of how the people the patient imagines them to be might act. All this was familiar to Shakespeare, who, in the passage I quoted in my first lecture, gives as an instance of imagination, or image-making, the lover who 'sees Helen's beauty in a brow of Egypt'. Yeats in three lines sums up both the lover's self-deception and its possible consequence:

> Maybe the bride-bed brings despair
> For each an imagined image brings
> And finds a real image there.

But I shall leave the pursuit of these, the most intimate of shadows, to your own imaginations.

The term 'psychological projection' may be a convenient one to apply when feeling-qualities are conferred by the individual, but it is hardly appropriate to the deliberate creations of *personae* by a social culture. When it is desirable that we should think of and feel towards particular individuals or classes of individuals in a special way, society tends to give them distinctive clothes, or uniforms. The effects of a uniform are both subtle and profound. A judge is not merely an elderly lawyer wearing a bizarre head-dress and a kind of overcoat dating from the remote past. His strange costume, because it is different from the clothes anyone else wears today, symbolizes his exceptional social function and powers; hence all who deal with him are confronted with an embodiment of society. The judge in court *is* something different in fact and feeling from the same man encountered on a social occasion. His professional *persona* is socially valuable, and his perceptual equipment contributes materially to it. The same is true of the priest, the policeman, and the postman, each in his different way. One of the most subtle examples of the effect of a uniform is the nurse. The sick person may be suddenly required to sacrifice his independence and to submit to the violation of his most intimate bodily privacy. The firm but gentle discipline this calls for is greatly facilitated by just that degree of depersonalization which a nurse's uniform gives her. She acquires an official *persona* which is less personal than her individuality, and which, while it in no way curbs her kindness, makes easier both her duties and the patient's submission to them. A nurse in uniform is both more and less than a woman.

In this lecture I have sought to show that much of what we perceive is our own contribution to the perceptual object, and that our attitude to people may be influenced by emotional characteristics which we imagine them to possess, or which society confers upon them. In my next lecture I shall discuss art as the embodiment of feelings in perceptual form, and the relationship between feeling and knowledge.

III

SYMBOL AND IMAGE

THE object of a philosophy of art in my view is not to increase anyone's appreciation of art, though it may do that to a limited extent, but to enlarge our understanding of man, and particularly of man as an artist and an enjoyer of art. I shall begin by considering the arts which appeal directly to the eye and the ear, painting, sculpture, and music, before I discuss the art which employs words, particularly poetry. Susanne Langer[31] has developed the idea which seems to owe something to Croce, that 'art is the creation of forms symbolic of human feeling'. In a more recent book[32] she says:

a work of art presents feeling . . . for our contemplation, making it visible or audible or in some way perceivable through a symbol, not inferable from a symptom. Artistic form is congruent with the dynamic forms of our direct sensuous, mental and emotional life; works of art are projections of 'felt life', as Henry James called it, into spatial, temporal, and poetic structures. They are images of feeling, that formulate it for our cognition. What is artistically good is whatever articulates and presents feeling to our understanding.

This statement takes us a long way towards an understanding of the nature of art, but if we ask how this process is brought about we shall see why it is in some ways inadequate. Let me quote from what I have written elsewhere: [33]

A work of art is said to cause feelings in the person who contemplates it, and 'beauty is in the eye of the beholder'. This, however, is again to confuse the physical and the perceptual world. Undoubtedly the physical object which constitutes the work of art, operating through its own particular physical medium, so influences the physical brain of the percipient that he experiences the feelings associated with its contemplation. The physical object which is a work of art is one thing and the feelings which it evokes are another. But this is not true of the world of perception, where, as we have seen, a perceptual object is itself subjective. In the perceptual world feelings can be embodied in concrete form. . . . So the artist, when creating a work of art in his own perceptual world, constructs it of his own *feelings* as well as his own visual, tactile or auditory sense-data. It is therefore a mistake to suppose that the feelings associated with perceiving a work of art are subjective in some way in which the sense-data comprising it are not. On this view a work of art is not *symbolic* of human feelings: it is literally an embodiment of them. A physical object is modified by the artist until it assumes in his perceptual world the form which embodies his feelings, so far as his competence as an artist allows. This physical object is then available to form representations in the perceptual worlds of other observers, where, in so far as their senses are acute, and their minds attuned by nature and experience to the mind of the artist, they will find similar feelings of their own embodied. In this way art is the communication of feelings.

Collingwood[34] puts the matter thus:

Theoretically the artist is a person who comes to know himself, to know his own emotion. This is also knowing his world, that is, the sights and sounds and so forth which together make up his total imaginative experience. The two knowledges are to him one knowledge, because these sights and sounds are to him steeped in the emotion with which he contemplates them: they are the language in which that emotion utters itself to his consciousness. His world is his language. What it says to him it says about himself; his imaginative vision of it is his self-knowledge.

And again:

The aesthetic experience . . . is also a making of oneself and of one's world, the self which was psyche being remade in the shape of consciousness, and the world, which was crude sensa, being remade in the shape of language, or sensa converted into imagery and charged with emotional significance.

This application of the sense-datum theory to art is so important that I must elaborate it somewhat. The crucial question is how the feelings of the artist can be embodied in a work of art. A work of art exists primarily in the mind of the artist; the sense-data, of which it is constructed, exist in his mind; the feelings with which they are associated are in his mind also. In so far as these feelings are linked with ideas, these ideas again are in his mind. The work of art in the mind of the artist, therefore, is a prehension, to use a term of Whitehead's, of sense-data and feelings with or without ideas, and it makes no difference whether it is fully imagined as a conception before the artist begins work on the physical object in which his conception is to be embodied, or whether the conception develops gradually while he works. When the work is complete it is for the artist a finished perceptual object, set in space like a picture, a statue, or a building, or requiring time for its performance, like a symphony. But being a perceptual object it is still an object in the artist's mind. All perceptual objects, however, as we have seen, are normally caused by physical objects. The artist, therefore, to create his perceptual object must either himself manipulate the physical canvas and pigments, or stone, or set the masons to work on his building, or an orchestra to produce the air vibrations through which alone his symphony can be expressed. The physical medium of an art, therefore, is no more to be identified with the work of art than the physical object which is perceived is to be identified with the sense-data by means of which it is perceived. The *physical medium* cannot embody the artist's feelings, and if we find it difficult to understand how the artist's feelings can be embodied in a work of art it will probably be because we are confusing the picture or the statue as a physical object with the same thing as a perceptual object. Indeed, the recalcitrance of the physical medium or the limitations of his technique may prevent the artist from fully realizing the complete expression of the feelings which formed the conception of his work of art.

But when the physical object has been modified by the artist's activity in such a way that it evokes in him a perceptual object which as far as possible embodies his feelings, the same physical object, meaning by that the identical one in the case of a picture or a sculpture, and a reproduction containing the same sound patterns, in the case of a piece of music, will tend to create in others who see or hear it a perceptual object embodying to a greater or less degree feelings similar to those which the work of art embodies for the artist.

By now it should be clear why I cannot accept Susanne Langer's view that works of art are symbols, but prefer the alternative view, which she puts forward in the same passage which I have quoted, that they are 'images of feeling'. A symbol is a sign which is arbitrarily accepted as standing for something else: an image is something which resembles something else and stands for it because of this resemblance. An 'image of feeling', therefore, can be an image only if it embodies feelings like those in which it originated, and, since feelings do not exist in the void, but are evoked by, or directed towards, something, the image of feeling which constitutes a work of art will include also something which the feeling is about. Thus to say even that a work of art is 'an image of feeling' is inadequate because it fails to take into account the object or idea to which the feeling is directed. Such an association is *an experience*, and a work of art is an image of an experience in which the representation of feeling plays an essential part. The whole experience is mental, and to try to distinguish in it a physical object and an emotional reaction to it is to dissect a living whole into abstractions.

The view which I have been putting forward illuminates many problems connected with art, and which those who are interested in the subject will find treated at greater length in Collingwood's book *The Principles of Art* and Susanne Langer's *Problems of Art*. I can now deal only briefly with some of them.

There is much discussion about the abstract, or non-representational element, in some modern art and we have become accustomed to the horror of elderly academicians whose surprise at what they describe as monstrosities seems never to grow less. Collingwood points out that 'people and things look different to us according to the emotion we feel in looking at them. . . . Photographs or literally accurate drawings of these things will be emotionally unlike them.' He distinguishes three degrees of representation: first, naïve or almost non-selective representation as exemplified in palaeolithic animal painting or Egyptian portrait sculpture; secondly, representation in which some emotional effect is produced by the bold selection of important features; while 'the third degree abandons literal representation altogether, but the work is still representative, because it aims this time with a single eye at emotional representation'. If we apply this to portraiture, 'a tactful painter will put in the appropriate exaggerations and so produce an emotionally correct likeness, correct, that is, for the particular audience he has in mind'. Here we are still dealing with art which aims at representation, and distinguishes between a photographic or mechanical likeness and one which cannot be that just because it has added to it the feelings evoked in the artist by the sitter. Now let us pass from that kind of representation to forms which bear a general resemblance to some familiar object, but embody also distortions which seem to many people unnatural and hence shocking, for example, some of Picasso's work and the sculpture of Henry Moore. There is an obvious parallel in much of the art of primitive peoples, and in some prehistoric art. It seems unlikely that primitive peoples create their strange distortions of the human figure in order to appear eccentric or shock the academicians of their tribe: they do it because it seems to them the natural way in which to create images expressive of emotion, and that, surely, is the object of Henry Moore and other artists who are using similar methods whether in two or three dimensions. Their works are representations not primarily of objects, but of feelings in relation to objects.

This leads naturally to the third type of art, in which the artist uses colours or shapes, or both, which are not recognizable as representing any known object. Such works provide no problem as long as we recognize that they are not seeking to represent natural objects, but only feelings, namely the feelings associated with the contemplation of those particular colours and shapes.

It is natural, therefore, that people who naïvely believe art to be concerned with the representation of people or things will be puzzled when a picture or sculpture does not present the appearance of people or things as they themselves see them; still more when it seems to them to be a gross distortion; and most of all when it appears to represent nothing at all. It could be argued that the belief that art should be in this sense representational is not a natural, but a sophisticated one, and that primitive people would have no difficulty in understanding modern art forms which puzzle our civilized contemporaries. However that may be, we shall not appreciate art, whether ancient, medieval, or modern, unless we seek to understand it as the creation of images embodying feelings. This, however, is a standard of criticism which is no whit less exacting than a purely representationalist one. It does not mean that a 'modern' artist because he uses a 'modern' technique either succeeds in representing feelings, nor, if he does, that the feelings he represents are worth entertaining by the observer. But if art is to be criticized, it should be on the right grounds. Sir Kenneth Clark's book,[35] *The Nude*, shows how remarkably the artistic representation of the human body has varied with the need to express changing feelings by means of it. 'Modern art', he concludes, 'shows even more explicitly than the art of the past that the nude does not simply represent the body but relates it, by analogy, to all structures that have become part of our imaginative experience.'

There is another aspect of visual perception which intimately concerns the visual arts. As I have said earlier, although visual percepts are primarily evoked through the eye, they include other than visual elements, because they have long been associated in experience with sense-data obtained through other senses. Thus, the visual appearance of an object, such as a book or an apple, implicitly conveys to us its feel and its weight. Moreover, its position in space sketches out, as it were, the potential movements which we should have to make in order to reach and grasp it, and movement involves time. Hence, what seems a simple visual percept is never purely visual, but includes memory-traces of other sense-data and is set within the space–time of a perceptual world common to all senses. This complexity is not normally discoverable on introspection, but is revealed when the perceptual process is broken down by disease of the brain. Collingwood[34] has drawn attention to the same fact in relation to art. 'The forgotten truth about painting', he writes, 'which was rediscovered by what may be called the Cézanne–Berenson approach to it was that the spectator's experience on looking at a picture is not a specifically visual experience at all. What he experiences does not consist of what he sees . . . it does not belong to sight alone, it belongs also (and on some occasions even more essentially) to touch.' He goes on to amplify this as meaning not only tactile values, but distance, space, and mass—motor sensations and images.

When we consider music we enter a sphere in which the creation of images is more difficult to understand. Music uses time in the same way as the plastic arts use space. But even as a structure in time the simplest melody is complex, and a symphony very complex indeed. We do not know why music should move us as it does. We get a hint perhaps from the fact that certain sounds and rhythms by themselves are moving, the insistent drumbeats of primitive dances, for example, the repetitive rhythms of rock and roll, and the synthetic sounds of *la musique concrète*. And attempts have been made to link these moving musical rhythms with the electrical rhythms of the emotional centres of the brain. Perhaps also we get a clue in the sensory relationships revealed by the drugs which produce hallucinations. Synaesthesiae, in which music influences visual percepts, may be merely the sensory overflow of what is normally a reverberation in the realm of emotion.

But the emotions evoked by music are not dependent solely upon simple and primitive rhythms, though these may find a place in the most complex music: they demand the exercise of a highly cultivated power of auditory discrimination, and a mind which can recognize and retain the development of melodies and themes.

The celestial logic of Bach is untranslatable into any other terms, for no one who has not experienced it, or is incapable of experiencing it, can be made to realize its quality by any verbal description. But here is what music meant to one master of words. Proust[36] writes:

The field open to the musician is not a miserable stave of seven notes, but an immeasurable keyboard (still, almost all of it unknown), on which, here and there only, separated by the gross darkness of its unexplored tracts, some few among the millions of keys, keys of tenderness, of passion, of courage, of serenity, which compose it, each one differing from the rest as one universe differs from another, have been discovered by certain great artists who do us the service, when they awaken in us the emotion corresponding to the theme which they have found, of showing us what richness, what variety, lies hidden unknown to us, in that great black impenetrable night, discouraging exploration, of our soul, which we have been content to regard as valueless and waste and void.

Of what, then, is music the image? It is the image of those feelings which Proust enumerated and of others besides. How it can thus represent them we do not precisely know, but its power to do so seems to spring from its relationship to time. Here is what a writer on music has to say about musical form:[37]

To me form in music means knowing at every moment exactly where we are. Consciousness of form is really a sense of orientation. . . . The conscious perception of trajectory is essential to the experience of musical form. The mind is exhilarated when feeling itself in gear, as it were, with the very impetus which gives rise to musical form, and when it discovers that pure abstract motion can be understood as a language with a world of images which are specifically its own.

Susanne Langer points out that 'musical movement is illusory, like volumes in pictorial space. By means of this purely apparent movement, music presents an auditory apparition of *time*', though this time, 'felt time', is quite unlike clock-time.

Can we not say that music, through its very relation to the structure of time itself, awakens echoes in that mystery which is the essence of our being, our life's transience and the inextinguishable hope that time itself is only a mode of apprehension? As Proust[36] put it in another passage: 'We shall perish, but we have for our hostages these divine captives who shall follow and share our fate. And death in their company is something less bitter, less inglorious, perhaps even less certain.'

This brings us to words, and I shall concern myself primarily with the use of words in poetry. Since poetry is an art, like painting, sculpture, or music, we may expect to find that it does what they do, but by using words instead of visual forms or musical sounds. Lewis,[38] writing as a poet turned critic, says:

The poet's re-creation includes both the object and the sensations connecting him with the object, both the facts and the tone of an experience: it is when object and sensation, happily married by him, breed an image in which *both* their likenesses appear, that something 'comes to us with an effect of revelation'.

Thus, for Lewis, the poetic image, expressed in words by means of metaphor, is of precisely the same nature as the image created in any other form of art. In another passage he writes:

Reality involves relationship, and as soon as you have relationship you have, for human beings, emotion; so that the poet cannot see things as they really are, cannot be precise about them, unless he is also precise about the feelings which attach him to them. It is this need for expressing the relationship between things and the relationship between things and feelings, which compels the poet to metaphor; and it is the same need, I suggest, which demands that within the poem the images should be linked by some internal necessity stronger than the mere tendency of words to congregate in patterns.

Poetic creation, therefore, is the creation of a particular kind of verbal image using for its purpose, of course, the arrangement of words in relation to rhythm, metre, rhyme, assonance, and so on; and, when the poet is successful, using individual images in such a way that the poem as a whole is itself a complex image.

If this is the right view of poetry it has several important consequences. The first is that, exactly as in the case of painting and sculpture, there is no rule about the intellectual or ideational content of a poem. It is irrelevant to the poetic process whether a poem embodies feelings about ideas or about objects. Similarly, we need not take sides between the Romantic movement in poetry and the Classical.[39] If the Romantic poet personifies Spring or Love or Death, he does it, unless he is merely following some pre-existing convention, because his own experience makes him feel that the appropriate image to express it is a personal one, and such a feeling surely has its roots deep in the animistic past of the human race. The continued popularity of the Romantic poets shows that it still survives.

If a poem is an image or a constellation of images, what bearing has that upon its meaning? Much has been written about the meaning of poetry. Richards[40] devotes a chapter to the definition of a poem. He points out that: 'The superstition which any language not intolerably prolix and uncouth encourages that there is something actual, *the poem*, which all readers have access to and upon which they pass judgment, misleads us.' He points out that we may be talking about the artist's experience, or about the experience of a qualified reader who made no mistakes, or about an ideal and perfect reader's possible experience, or about our own actual experience. The question which of these possible definitions of a poem we should adopt is, in his view, 'one of convenience merely; but it is by no means easy to decide'. He himself reaches a conclusion with which he does not seem very satisfied, since he describes it as 'odd and complicated', namely, that a poem is 'a class of experiences which do not differ in any character more than a certain amount, varying for each character, from a standard experience. We may take as this standard experience the relevant experience of the poet when contemplating the completed composition.' A more recent writer, Redpath,[41] says very much the same thing in somewhat different words.

> The *meaning* of a poem [he says], then, like its value, is something which we shall only arrive at if we make a right aesthetic decision. . . . In making which we have given due weight (whether by careful consideration or by some more or less automatic process) to the different factors involved, in determining that class of experience one or other of which the words of the poem, in that order, and in that form, *ought to evoke* in a reader familiar with the language (or languages) in which the poem is written.

I suggest that the fact that individual words have meanings, and that meanings can be attached to the words used in making a poem, has deceived those who think that a poem itself must have meaning; and further that a poem being an image, when once it has been created, exists in its own right, for the contemplation of anyone and everyone. And since its creation involves a considerable amount of unconscious activity on the part of the poet it is by no means certain that the poet is fully aware of its significance for himself. A poem, therefore, has no meaning other than itself, and what it is is what the reader or hearer experiences when he reads or hears it. This, I think, is what Walter de la Mare[42] meant when he said: 'Why must the poem have a meaning? We don't ask what is the meaning of a piece of music—why of a poem?'

Joyce Cary[43] in *Art and Reality* applies to literature, chiefly the novel, a theory of art essentially similar to that which I am now expressing. 'If any truth about quality,' he writes, 'about the feeling as well as the fact, is to be conveyed from person to person, it can only be done within the realm of personality, of emotional and sensible forms, which is the world of art.'

There are other applications of this which I should have liked to discuss, if I had had time. The stage is a good example of a perceptual space which through the dramatist's art becomes an imaginary space with dimensions both identical with, and totally different from, the few cubic yards of the theatre by which it is mediated. And the dance translates the rhythms of music into visible forms, which speak not only through those rhythms but also with the language of the body, and transport the onlooker for a few brief moments into an ideal world beyond the clumsiness and frailty of our common humanity.

Valéry[44] in one of his Socratic dialogues puts into the mouth of Socrates, who is watching some dancers, these words, which illuminate not only the dance but also art itself:

If some Reason were to dream, standing hard, erect, her eye armed, her mouth shut, mistress of her lips,—would not her dream be what we are now looking at?—this world of measured forces and studied illusions?—A dream, a dream, but all charged with symmetries, all order, all acts, all sequences! . . . Who can tell what august Laws are here dreaming that they have clothed their faces with brightness and agreed to make manifest to mortals how the real, the unreal, and the intelligible can fuse and combine, obedient to the power of the Muses?

I am now approaching the question which lies at the heart of this lecture, and, indeed, of these three lectures. If art is the creation of images, of what are they images? But before I consider that I must look at a distinction which has greatly influenced thought in many fields during the last thirty years. Ogden and Richards[45] in *The Meaning of Meaning* distinguish between what they call the symbolic and the emotive use of words. 'The symbolic use of words', they say, 'is *statement*; the recording, the support, the organisation and the communication of references. The emotive use of words is a more simple matter, it is the use of words to express or excite feelings and attitudes.' They go on to say that, although the two functions usually occur together, none the less they are in principle distinct. They then draw attention to the frequency with which these two functions are in their view confused, and continue: 'It ought to be impossible to talk about poetry or religion as though they were capable of giving knowledge. . . . A poem—or a religion . . . has no concern with limited and directed reference. It tells us, or should tell us, nothing. . . . What it does, or should do, is to induce a fitting attitude to experience.' Few words which have had so much influence can have begged so many questions. I have not time now to discuss them all. What is relevant to our present purpose is the statement that neither poetry nor religion is capable of giving knowledge.

There are many kinds of knowledge. Our knowledge of the physical world, as we have seen, is obtained by means of perceptual objects. It is of the essence of knowledge that it should consist of a bringing together of a subject and an object. The subject is not only modified by the object; he is modified in such a way that some characteristic of the object becomes part of his consciousness. Sensory perception exemplifies these two elements. The arrangement of sense-data in perceptual space is a representation of the structure of the corresponding physical objects in physical space; the qualitative features of perceptual objects, such as their colour and feel, are supplied by the subject and serve the purpose of making possible the discrimination of the structure of the physical world. Moreover, the subject's perceptual space is a perspective of which he is himself the focus, and which orientates his actions, potential or actual, towards his environment.

The products of the creative artist, as again we have seen, are images of a more complex kind, since they use sense-data or words to embody or express the feelings of the artist in relation to the ideas or objects which arouse them. They are thus images of experiences—experiences of perceptual objects, ideas, and feelings fused together. The word 'knowledge' may have acquired too narrowly propositional a meaning to be considered appropriate to this experience, yet the experience is again an example of the subject–object relationship. And is it altogether inappropriate to call this 'knowledge'? The artist is peculiar, not in having such experiences, though he commonly has them with exceptional intensity, but in also being able to embody them in images, and so communicate them. But if other people did not have these experiences spontaneously in some degree the artist's images would mean nothing to them.

We are now faced by the contrast between the image and the symbol, and also that between apprehension and comprehension to which Shakespeare drew attention in the passage I quoted in my first lecture. On the one hand the images employed by art and poetry enable us to apprehend experiences in which objects, thoughts, and feelings are blended: on the other hand physical science employs symbols to convey to us the structure of a physical world, which is inferred from our perceptual experiences, but of which it tells us that we can know nothing more about these multifarious physical events than their structure. But there is one most important exception to this generalization. It is possible at one point to bridge the gulf between the direct apprehension inherent in consciousness and the indirect apprehension by means of which science presents to us the inferred structure of the physical world; for there is one point at which the two meet, namely, in the brain of the percipient. In this connexion it does not, I think, matter whether we take the view that consciousness is really a name for certain states of the brain, or is the result of the inter-action between those brain states and an independent mind. In either case the immediate content of consciousness is always a particular state of the brain. It is true that what we are directly aware of in our own brains seems very different from anything likely to occur in the soft greyish-pink substance which we see when we look at someone else's brain, but this need not surprise us, for when I look at you you do not look to me in the least like the thoughts which I hope you are at this moment entertaining. We have still much to learn about the nature of the brain states which determine the content of consciousness, but we know enough already to be reasonably sure that they consist of patterns of electrical impulses, or electrical fields, of great complexity. That is to say, redness, for example, is such a pattern and therefore a certain structure of events in space–time. If this view is correct we can at least say that we do have direct experience of some such physical structures and they are of the kind with which we are familiar in the varied sensations, thoughts, and feelings which compose our states of consciousness. This raises many questions, which I cannot now pursue farther.

Finally, we reach the question whether there are yet other modes of apprehension, or whether, to put the question in another way, either images or symbols or both combined give us knowledge of the nature of things beyond both our immediate experiences and the structure of the physical world revealed by science. Some modern philosophers regard this as a meaningless question and it would take me too long now to discuss that aspect of it. Let me rather see what such a question might imply. All religions and some philosophers assume that the conception of the totality of things is meaningful. All the great religions are highly complex structures composed of philosophical ideas, beliefs about historical events, symbols and images, and the emotions they evoke. There are thus certain analogies between religion and art, particularly poetry.[46] But whereas art claims only to represent experience without implying that the experience represented has any validity beyond itself, religion also resembles science in that it claims that its symbols refer to the nature of something beyond them, namely the universe as a whole. The representation of the whole by one of its parts presents considerable philosophical difficulties, but an analogy may be of help here. As we have just seen, in all our conscious experiences we are directly aware of what may be called samples of the structure of physical events in space–time. From these science has inferred all that we now know about the nature of the physical structure of the universe. There seems no reason why, taking all the experiences of our lives as samples of the structure of the universe as revealed to thought and feeling combined, we should not make inferences as to the nature of that which underlies our experiences and the physical structure about which science teaches us.

We may all agree that the reasons which induce any particular individual to accept the beliefs of any religion are complex and varied and differ from one person to another. No man, if he would, can start and work things out for himself; the most he can do is to accept or reject one of the elaborate systems of ideas which he finds already in existence. Religions, however, are not initially constructed by philosophers, but grow out of experiences which philosophers subsequently may seek to interpret. And it is doubtful whether without such experiences any religion could survive. These experiences are themselves of more than one kind, but among them those which are termed mystical are perhaps fundamental. A dictionary defines mysticism as 'the doctrine that the ultimate nature of reality . . . may be known in an immediate apprehension', but I believe it would be wrong to exclude from this category apprehensions which are of the same kind except that they are mediated by experiences of nature or of human relationships. Such apprehensions are not peculiar to any one religion, though the believer will naturally interpret them in terms of his own system of beliefs. Indeed, they are not restricted to those who profess a religious belief; and if it is possible for any of our experiences to be images of the nature of the totality of things, it is hard to believe that the occurrence of such apprehensions should be determined by the nature of the system of ideas used to interpret them. And here, surely, in part, lies their strength. For this reason in this context I shall try to illustrate the variety of mystical apprehension even within what may be broadly called the Judaeo-Christian tradition. There is the climax of the book of Job in those chapters, the 38th to the 41st, in which the Lord answers Job out of the whirlwind, and challenges him with all the magnificence and mystery of the universe. And in quieter tone there is the 13th chapter of the Wisdom of Solomon, which condemns men who by considering the works did not acknowledge the work-master: 'With whose beauty if they being delighted took them to be gods, let them know how much better the Lord of them is: for the first author of beauty has created them.' And coming nearer to our own day we find the same apprehension in men as diverse as Spinoza and St. John of the Cross, George Fox and Traherne, William Harvey and Goethe, Wordsworth, Blake, and Keats, Whitehead and Sherrington. When Sherrington[47] came to consider mind he found it impossible to explain in terms of neurophysiology, but he could discover no explanation for it elsewhere. Mind remained, therefore, an irreducible surd of his thought. 'Mind, for anything perception can compass', he wrote, 'goes therefore in our spatial world more ghostly than a ghost.' And mind, though the product of nature, must often be in conflict with nature. 'No other mind is equal, let alone superior to it': natural religion, therefore, 'sublimes personal Deity, to Deity wholly impersonal'. Yet the poet in Sherrington could not be quite satisfied with this conclusion of the thinker, as one sentence in *Man on his Nature* reveals. When he makes Nature address man he puts into her mouth these, as her last words: 'Bethink you too that perhaps in knowing me you do but know the instrument of a Purpose, the tool of a Hand too large for sight as now to compass. Try then to teach your sight to grow.'

Those who experience these apprehensions find that they are their own validation. But that need not prevent the philosopher from asking how they can be so, as long as he does not believe his failure to answer this question invalidates them.

As in art, but hardly at all in science, feelings play a large part in these experiences, and most philosophers today believe that feelings are purely subjective, and tell us nothing about the nature of the objects which evoke them. I have shown that this is not true of works of art, which are images of feelings because they embody feelings. And this perhaps leads to a broader generalization. Feelings *can* give us knowledge: they can give us knowledge of feelings—and only feelings can do so. To say that a man is angry is partly to describe his actual or potential behaviour—that he grows red in the face, shouts, and waves his arms about. But since I have been angry myself, to be told that a man is angry is to *know* to some extent how he feels, to form an image, that is to imagine his feelings. If, as I believe, Collingwood is right when he says: 'The proposition, understood as a form of words expressing thought and not emotion, and as constituting the unit of scientific discourse, is a fictitious entity', it follows that images will in general provide a more adequate representation of many aspects of life than symbols, though symbols, of course, may play a part in creating images, as words do in poetry. And if feeling is itself a constituent of that which we are seeking to know, we can have true knowledge of it only if feeling is an ingredient in our knowing experience. If the universe itself is of such a nature, we can have no adequate knowledge of it without feeling.

This brings me back to the dolphins and flying-fish, which I described in my first lecture, flashing in and out of my thoughts as I sailed home from South Africa, the dolphins leaping in lovely curves from the waves, and the flying-fish rising in company from the sea into the sunlight, shaking the shining drops from their wings. To me they were images as well as objects, and it is the mystery of beauty that it should be an image, as many have felt, of the nature of things, triumphant over all the accidents and agonies of life.

Let me end with the last verse of Walter de la Mare's poem 'Fare Well'.

> Look thy last on all things lovely,
> Every hour. Let no night
> Seal thy sense in deathly slumber
>   Till to delight
> Thou have paid thy utmost blessing;
> Since that all things thou wouldst praise
> Beauty took from those who loved them
>   In other days.

In these lines, and those which precede them in this poem, the poet looks unfalteringly at the transience of life and 'all things lovely', but finds that beauty is stronger than time, for it is beauty which takes them away. 'Beauty took': are these words outmoded Romanticism, semantic impropriety, philosophical nonsense, at the worst illusion, at the best a sigh? Or do they express the final apprehension and comprehension?

REFERENCES AND NOTES

1. A. N. WHITEHEAD, *Science and the Modern World*, Cambridge, 1932, pp. 68–69.

2. A. S. EDDINGTON, *The Nature of the Physical World*, London, 1935, p. 5.

3. BERTRAND RUSSELL, *Human Knowledge, its Scope and Limits*, London, 1948, pp. 217 et seq. Russell's views on perception have recently been summarized in a broadcast lecture, 'The World and the Observer', published in *The Listener*, lix (1958), p. 223, 6 February.

4. F. H. GEORGE, 'Epistemology and the Problem of Perception', *Mind*, lxvi (1957), p. 491.

5. W. RUSSELL BRAIN, *Mind, Perception and Science*, Oxford, 1951, p. 4.

6. E. D. ADRIAN, *The Basis of Sensation*, London, 1938.

7. BERTRAND RUSSELL, *The Problems of Philosophy*, London, 1912.

8. R. H. WARD, *A Drug-taker's Notes*, London, 1957.

9. W. MAYER-GROSS, 'Experimental Psychoses and other Mental Abnormalities produced by Drugs', *British Medical Journal*, ii (1951), p. 317.

10. The following quotations are taken from W. Penfield and H. Jasper's *Epilepsy and the Functional Anatomy of the Human Brain*, London, 1954.

11. Quoted by E. GUTTMANN in 'Artificial Psychoses produced by Mescaline', *Journal of Mental Science*, lxxxii (1936), p. 203.

12. Quoted by Mayer-Gross (9) above.

13. W. GREY WALTER, *The Living Brain*, London, 1953, p. 68.

14. J. R. SMYTHIES, 'A Logical and Cultural Analysis of Hallucinatory Sense Experience', *Journal of Mental Science*, cii (1956), p. 336.

15. R. J. HIRST, 'Perception, Science and Common Sense', *Mind*, lx (1951), p. 481.

16. J. R. SMYTHIES, 'A Note on R. J. Hirst's recent paper in *Mind*', *Mind*, lxiii (1954), p. 388.

17. G. RYLE, *The Concept of Mind*, London, 1949.

18. G. RYLE, *Dilemmas*, Cambridge, 1954.

19. G. A. PAUL, 'Is There a Problem about Sense-data?' in *Essays in Logic and Language*, ed. by Antony Flew, Oxford, 1951.

20. A. G. N. FLEW, 'The Extension of Mind: Comments on Dr. J. R. Smythies' Paper', *Journal of the Society for Psychical Research*, xxxvi (1952), p. 547.

21. M. LEAN, *Sense Perception and Matter*, London, 1953.

22. A. M. QUINTON, 'The Problem of Perception', *Mind*, lxiv (1955), p. 28.

23. A. J. AYER, *The Problem of Knowledge*, London, 1956.

24. A. N. WHITEHEAD, *Adventures of Ideas*, Cambridge, 1939, pp. 276–81.

25. C. D. BROAD, *Scientific Thought*, London, 1927, pp. 543–4. Recent discussions of physical and perceptual space are to be found in *Analysis of Perception*, by J. R. Smythies, London, 1956, and *Brain and Consciousness*, by H. Kuhlenbeck, Basel and New York, 1957.

26. RYLE and others lay great stress upon the words habitually used to describe perceptual experiences, believing that the nature of perception can be logically deduced from them.

There was no time in these lectures to deal with this aspect of the subject, but I have done so briefly elsewhere (5). E. M. Adams, in a recent paper on 'The Nature of the Sense-datum Theory' published in *Mind*, lxvii (1958), p. 216, has demonstrated the invalidity of such arguments. 'The Sense-datum theory', he writes, 'is a proposed categorical system, a special philosophical theory designed to render consistent what was believed to be an incompatibility in the basic epistemological and ontological categories of the common-sense framework, namely an incompatibility between what it is to know and what the external world is, so that knowledge of the external world becomes highly problematic if not impossible.'

27. J. R. SMYTHIES, 'Analysis of Projection', *British Journal of Philosophy of Science*, v (1954), p. 120.

28. F. ALEXANDER, *Fundamentals of Psychoanalysis*, New York, 1938.

29. R. L. MUNROE, *Schools of Psychoanalytic Thought*, London, 1957.

30. E. KRETSCHMER, *Textbook of Medical Psychology*, translated by E. B. Strauss, London, 1934.

31. SUSANNE LANGER, *Feeling and Form*, London, 1953.

32. SUSANNE LANGER, *Problems of Art*, London, 1957.

33. W. RUSSELL BRAIN, 'Perception and Imperception', *Journal of Mental Science*, cii (1956), p. 228.

34. R. G. COLLINGWOOD, *The Principles of Art*, Oxford, 1938.

35. KENNETH CLARK, *The Nude: A Study of Ideal Art*, London, 1956.

36. MARCEL PROUST, *Remembrance of Things Past*, Volume 2. *Swann's Way*, Part 2, London, 1951, pp. 183 and 184.

37. ROBERTO GERHARD, 'The Nature of Music', *The Score*, No. 16 (1956), p. 7.

38. C. DAY LEWIS, *The Poetic Image*, London, 1947.

39. The view of art based upon the sense-datum theory and expressed in this lecture illuminates the nature of the Romantic movement and its successors. John Bayley, writing in *The Romantic Survival*, London, 1957, says: 'The premises on which any romantic poem is written are an acute consciousness of the isolated creating self on the one hand, and of a world unrelated and possibly uninterested and hostile on the other, and the wish somehow to achieve a harmonious synthesis of the two.' But if this is the essence of the art of all poets, the difference between the Romantic and the Classical cannot be as great as some would maintain. Perhaps it lies, not in the process, but in the poet's attitude to it and his use of it.

40. I. A. RICHARDS, *Principles of Literary Criticism*, 9th impression, London, 1947.

41. J. REDPATH, *Some Problems of Modern Aesthetics* in *British Philosophy in Mid-Century*, edited by C. A. Mace, London, 1957.

42. RUSSELL BRAIN, *Tea with Walter de la Mare*, London, 1957.

43. JOYCE CARY, *Art and Reality*, Cambridge, 1958. Cary combined the training of an artist with experience as a novelist. He was indebted to Croce, but not being himself a philosopher, he did not achieve a coherent philosophical view of art nor did he analyse what he meant by intuition or symbol. Nevertheless, his book is full of pregnant insights into the part played by what he calls the symbol, but I should prefer to term the image, in art.

44. PAUL VALÉRY, *Dance and the Soul*, translated by Dorothy Bussy, London, 1951. The original of the passage I have quoted runs: 'Que si une Raison rêvait, dure, debout, l'œil armé, et la bouche fermée, comme maîtresse de ses lèvres, — le songe qu'elle ferait ne serait-ce point ce que nous voyons maintenant, — ce monde de forces exactes et d'illusions étudiées? — Rêve, rêve, mais rêve tout pénétré de symétries, tout ordre, tout actes et séquences! . . . Qui sait quelles Lois augustes rêvent ici qu'elles ont pris de clairs visages, et qu'elles s'accordent dans le dessein de manifester aux mortels comment le réel, l'irréel et l'intelligible se peuvent fondre et combiner selon la puissance des Muses?' Here Valéry allows Socrates to see in the dance a Romantic power which he was unwilling to accord to poetry.

45. C. K. OGDEN and I. A. RICHARDS, *The Meaning of Meaning*, 2nd ed., London, 1927, pp. 149 and 158.

46. This question is discussed in a recent book, *Metaphysical Beliefs*, by Stephen E. Toulmin, Ronald W. Hepburn, and Alasdair Macintyre, London, 1957, and especially in the section by Ronald W. Hepburn entitled 'Poetry and Religious Belief'.

47. SIR CHARLES SHERRINGTON, *Man on his Nature*, Cambridge, 1942.

PRINTED IN GREAT BRITAIN
AT THE UNIVERSITY PRESS, OXFORD
BY VIVIAN RIDLER
PRINTER TO THE UNIVERSITY